Yukon Ho!

A Calvin and Hobbes Collection
by Bill Watterson

SCHOLASTIC INC.
New York Toronto London Auckland Sydney

Calvin and Hobbes is syndicated internationally
by Universal Press Syndicate.

ISBN 0-590-44168-X

12 11   3/0

Printed in the U.S.A.

First Scholastic printing, January 1991

The Yukon Song

My tiger friend has got the sled,
And I have packed a snack.
We're all set for the trip ahead.
We're never coming back!

We're abandoning this life we've led!
So long, Mom and Pop!
We're sick of doing what you've said,
And now it's going to stop!

We're going where it snows all year,
Where life can have real meaning.
A place where we won't have to hear,
"Your room could stand some cleaning."

The Yukon is the place for us!
That's where we want to live.
Up there we'll get to yell and cuss,
And act real primitive.

We'll never have to go to school,
Forced into submission,
By monstrous, crabby teachers who'll
Make us learn addition.

We'll never have to clean a plate,
Of veggie glops and goos.
Messily we'll masticate,
Using any fork we choose!

The timber wolves will be our friends.
We'll stay up late and howl,
At the moon, till nighttime ends,
Before going on the prowl.

Oh, what a life! We cannot wait,
To be in that arctic land,
Where we'll be masters of our fate,
And lead a life that's grand!

No more of parental rules!
We're heading for some snow!
Good riddance to those grown-up ghouls!
We're leaving! *Yukon Ho!*

Calvin and HObbEs

by WATTERSON

WHEW! THIS MUST BE THE BIGGEST HILL IN THE STATE!

KIND OF FRUSTRATING, ISN'T IT? I WISH DAD WOULD GET TRANSFERRED TO THE ANDES.

LET'S GO DOWN THE HILL AND SEE IF WE CAN TRAVEL INTO THE FUTURE.

GO INTO THE FUTURE? HOW?

IT'S EASY! ALL WE HAVE TO DO IS GET GOING REAL FAST AND WE'LL TIME-WARP!

HA HA! FASTER! FASTER!

GOSH, WHAT DO YOU SUPPOSE THE FUTURE WILL BE LIKE?

WHO KNOWS? FLYING CARS AND CITIES BUILT ON CLOUDS, MAYBE!

JUST THINK OF ALL THE WEIRD THINGS WE CAN TELL PEOPLE WE SAW! OH BOY!

HEY, WE'RE AT THE BOTTOM OF THE HILL. I DIDN'T FEEL ANY TIME WARP, DID YOU?

NOPE.

BUT LOOK! IT'S TWO MINUTES LATER THAN WHEN WE STARTED! WE'RE IN THE FUTURE!!

HMM...THINGS HAVEN'T IMPROVED. I'M DISAPPOINTED.

5

I COULDN'T READ IT BECAUSE MY PARENTS FORGOT TO PAY THE GRAVITY BILL.

MAKE A PREDICTION, HOBBES.

WHAT FOR?

SO WE CAN SEE IF YOU HAVE ESP.

OK, I PREDICT YOU'LL FIND AN IRRESISTIBLE ATTRACTION TO A MUD HOLE.

!

HA HA. YOU STAY AWAY FROM ME.

IT'S GOING TO COME TRUE! I CAN FEEL IT!

Calvin and Hobbes

by WATTERSON

"BEFORE BEGINNING ANY HOME-PLUMBING REPAIR, MAKE SURE YOU POSSESS THE PROPER TOOLS FOR THE JOB."

"CHECK THE FOLLOWING LIST OF HANDY EXPLETIVES, AND SEE THAT YOU KNOW HOW TO USE THEM."

CALVIN WAKES UP ONE MORNING TO FIND HE NO LONGER EXISTS IN THE THIRD DIMENSION! HE IS **2-D**!

THINNER THAN A SHEET OF PAPER, CALVIN HAS NO SURFACE AREA ON THE BOTTOM OF HIS FEET! HE IS IMMOBILE!

ONLY BY "WAVING" HIS BODY CAN CALVIN CREATE ENOUGH FRICTION WITH THE GROUND TO MOVE!

HAVING WIDTH BUT NO THICKNESS, CALVIN IS VULNERABLE TO THE SLIGHTEST GUST OF WIND!

TO AVOID DRAFTS, HE TWISTS HIMSELF INTO A TUBE, AND ROLLS ACROSS THE FLOOR!

WATTERSON

SOMEONE IS COMING! CALVIN QUICKLY STANDS UP STRAIGHT.

TURNING PERFECTLY SIDEWAYS, HE IS A NEARLY INVISIBLE VERTICAL LINE! NO ONE WILL NOTICE!

HEY DAD, KNOW WHY YOU DIDN'T SEE ME ALL MORNING?? I WAS TWO-DIMENSIONAL!

HMMM, I'LL BET YOU CAN'T DO IT ALL AFTERNOON, TOO...

DEAR!

9

TIME FOR BED, CALVIN.

IT'S A FREE COUNTRY. I CAN DO WHAT I WANT.

GOOD NIGHT.

COMMUNISTS!

OH NO, I HAVE TO GO TO THE BATHROOM! THE MONSTERS WILL GET ME AS SOON AS I SET FOOT ON THE FLOOR!

I KNOW! PUT YOUR PILLOW DOWN AS A DECOY. WHILE THEY'RE EATING THAT, YOU CAN SLIP OUT!

GREAT IDEA!

I'M COMING OUT OF BED NOW! HERE I AM, ALL FAT AND SQUISHY!

THEY TOOK IT! MAN, LOOK AT THE FEATHERS FLY! YOU'D BETTER HURRY!

NO, I'VE DECIDED TO STAY HERE AND WET THE BED. BUT IT'S OK WITH ME IF YOU DON'T WANT TO STAY.

BOMBARDED BY HIGH-ENERGY PHOTONS, CALVIN IS TRANSFORMED INTO A LIVING X-RAY!

ALTHOUGH THIS CONDITION WILL FACILITATE FUTURE MEDICAL DIAGNOSES, IT DOES MAKE CALVIN'S PRESENCE AT THE DINNER TABLE A DISGUSTING ORDEAL!

EVERYONE CAN SEE CALVIN'S FOOD BEING GROUND INTO MUSHY PULP AND SWALLOWED! AT THIS MOMENT, CALVIN CHEWS UP A LARGE SPOONFUL OF CREAMED CORN!

FOR GOSH SAKES, CLOSE YOUR MOUTH WHEN YOU CHEW!! YOU THINK WE WANT TO SEE THAT?!

MKGHH! SMACK! BLAGHKH!

calvin and HobbEs
by WATTERSON

I'M GOING OUTSIDE, MOM!

HOLD ALL MY CALLS.

CALVIN LOOKS AROUND. SOMETHING IS DIFFERENT.

THE ODD-COLORED TREE BEHIND HIM SLOWLY LIFTS UP! IT'S NOT A TREE AT ALL! IT'S A LEG!

OH NO! CALVIN IS THE SIZE OF A BUG *TO* A BUG! HE RUNS FOR HIS LIFE!

A CLAW CRASHES WITH DEAFENING IMPACT! THE BUG IS TRYING TO STEP ON CALVIN! WHAT A HORRIBLE FATE!

CALVIN SCRAMBLES MADLY, PROMISING HIMSELF THAT HE'LL NEVER SQUISH ANOTHER BUG IF HE LIVES TO RETURN TO NORMAL SIZE!

SUDDENLY IN A SPRAY OF SLIME, THE BUG IS GONE! A MONSTROUS FROG LICKS ITS CHOPS! CALVIN IS SAVED!

AACGK! WHAT'S THAT ON MY PLATE?! GOOD HEAVENS, GET IT OFF THE TABLE!!

BUT MOM, FROGS ARE OUR *FRIENDS!*

15

OK, I THINK THAT'S DAD'S BUILDING UP AHEAD.

I'M NOT SURE WHERE HIS OFFICE IS, SO WE'LL JUST HAVE TO LOOK IN THE WINDOWS AS WE ZIP BY.

HEY! THERE HE IS! THERE'S DAD! HI, DAD! DAD, LOOK! OUT THE WINDOW!!

DARN IT! HE'S STILL READING THAT BRIEF. LOOK OUT THE WINDOW, DAD!

DID YOU BRING ANY ROCKS? I DIDN'T THINK TO.

HEY DAD! LOOK OUT THE WINDOW! ...I CAN'T BELIEVE HE'S JUST SITTING IN THERE.

WHY DOESN'T HE LOOK UP?

I GUESS HE'S PRETTY BUSY.

YEAH, BUT WE CAN'T SIT UP HERE ALL DAY! SHEESH. LET'S GO.

IF HE HAD NOTICED US, WE COULD'VE GIVEN HIM A RIDE HOME.

HMPH, I SAY LET HIM TAKE THE SMELLY OL' BUS IF HE CAN'T EVEN LOOK OUT THE WINDOW ONCE IN A WHILE. SERVES HIM RIGHT.

I'M HOME!

DAD! HOBBES AND I FLEW BY YOUR OFFICE WINDOW TODAY ON A RUG! WE SAW YOU WORKING.

WE WAVED AND HOLLERED, BUT YOU DIDN'T EVEN LOOK UP. WE COULDN'T BELIEVE IT. YOU MISSED THE WHOLE THING!

I THOUGHT WE WERE CUTTING DOWN HIS SUGAR INTAKE.

1988 ISN'T TOO FAR AWAY, DAD.

 IF YOU'RE THINKING OF RUNNING FOR "DAD" AGAIN, YOU'D BETTER GET YOUR CAMPAIGN IN GEAR.

 FRANKLY, THE POLLS LOOK GRIM. I DON'T THINK YOU'VE GOT MUCH OF A SHOT AT KEEPING THE OFFICE.

 I TAKE COMFORT IN THE FACT THAT NOT MANY PEOPLE WOULD WANT IT.

FLIPPANT REMARKS HAVE A WAY OF HAUNTING CANDIDATES, YOU KNOW.

 THE CHAMELEON SITS MOTIONLESS.

 AMAZINGLY, THE LIZARD CHANGES COLOR TO BLEND IN WITH HIS SURROUNDINGS.

 MOMENTS LATER, HE IS VIRTUALLY INVISIBLE.

 I SEE YOU HIDING BACK THERE! NOW COME CLEAN UP THIS MESS YOU MADE IN THE KITCHEN!

 HOLD STILL. THERE'S A MONSTER HORSEFLY ON YOUR HEAD.

 POW!!

 CAN YOU BELIEVE IT? I *MISSED!*

!

 SO EXCUSE *ME* FOR TRYING TO HELP! YOU WANNA SCRATCH A STINGING WELT ALL DAY? *FINE!* GO AWAY!

NO, WAIT. THERE'S A MOSQUITO ON YOU.

Calvin and Hobbes

by WATTERSON

THE DREADED SCUM BEINGS FIRE! SPACEMAN SPIFF IS *HIT!*

IT NEVER FAILS. I JUST WASHED AND WAXED THIS THING.

OUR HERO, THE INTREPID SPACEMAN SPIFF, STRUGGLES WITH THE CONTROLS OF HIS DAMAGED SPACECRAFT!

THE FREEM PROPULSION BLASTERS ARE USELESS! SPIFF CRASHES ONTO THE SURFACE OF AN ALIEN PLANET!

UNSCATHED, THE FEARLESS SPACE EXPLORER EMERGES FROM THE SMOLDERING WRECKAGE! HE IS MAROONED ON A HOSTILE WORLD!

SCORCHED BY TWIN SUNS, THE PLANET IS NOTHING BUT BARREN ROCK AND METHANE! THERE'S NO HOPE OF FINDING FOOD OR WATER!

SPIFF COLLAPSES! OH NO, A HIDEOUS ALIEN SPOTS HIM! IN HIS WEAKENED STATE, SPIFF IS NO MATCH FOR THE MONSTER! *THIS COULD BE THE END!!*

LUNCHTIME! I BROUGHT YOU A SANDWICH AND SOME LEMONADE.

BRING THE DISHES BACK WHEN YOU'RE DONE, OK?

...OH WELL.

THANKS, MOM.

QUICK, MOM! ALIENS JUST LANDED IN THE BACKYARD! THEY DEMAND TO TALK TO YOU!

YOU GO ON OUT! I'LL GUARD THE COOKIES IN THE KITCHEN!

QUICK! HURRY!

SHE'S NOT BUYING THIS.

CALVIN, JUST HOW DUMB DO YOU THINK I AM?

WHAT DO YOU THINK IS THE SECRET TO HAPPINESS? IS IT MONEY, POWER OR FAME?

I'D CHOOSE MONEY. IF YOU HAVE ENOUGH MONEY, YOU CAN BUY POWER AND FAME. THAT WAY YOU'D HAVE IT ALL AND BE REALLY HAPPY!

HAPPINESS IS BEING FAMOUS FOR YOUR FINANCIAL ABILITY TO INDULGE IN EVERY KIND OF EXCESS.

I SUPPOSE THAT'S ONE WAY TO DEFINE IT.

THE PART I THINK I'D LIKE BEST IS CRUSHING PEOPLE WHO GET IN MY WAY.

LOOK! SOMEBODY POURED NEW CEMENT!

IS ANYONE LOOKING? WE COULD WRITE OUR INITIALS IN IT, OR MAKE A HAND PRINT, OR SOMETHING!

YEAH! "OR SOMETHING"!

I THINK WE'D BETTER FIND A HOSE QUICK!

I DIDN'T THINK IT WOULD SET UP SO FAST.

HEY CALVIN, WHATCHA DOIN'?

SHHH!

QUIET DOWN OR YOU'LL GIVE AWAY MY POSITION. HOBBES AND I ARE HAVING A WATER FIGHT.

A WATER FIGHT! CAN I PLAY?

YOU? HA! WAR IS A *MANLY* ART!

I SUPPOSE ANYTHING SO IDIOTIC WOULD *HAVE* TO BE. CAN I PLAY IN YOUR GAME OR NOT?

I DON'T KNOW, IT SEEMS YOU'D RATHER BE MAKING SMART REMARKS.

C'MON, CAN'T I JOIN YOUR WATER FIGHT? I HAVE MY OWN WATER PISTOL AND EVERYTHING! IT'LL JUST TAKE ME A MINUTE TO GET IT.

OK, YOU CAN PLAY, BUT HOBBES IS ON *MY* TEAM. YOU HAVE TO FIGHT BOTH OF US.

GREAT! I CAN BEAT YOU AND YOUR STUFFED TIGER ANY DAY. I'LL GO PUT ON MY SWIMSUIT.

SUSIE'S GOING TO PLAY WITH US, OK?

OH BOY. GIRLS FLIP FOR GUYS IN JAMS.

I GOT MY WATER PISTOL! I'M ALL SET!

GOOD. NOW HOBBES AND I WILL BE ONE TEAM, AND YOU...

LOOK AT YOUR TOY TIGER! HE'S WEARING *JAMS*!! THAT'S SO *CUTE!* LET ME SQUEEZE HIM!

OH FOR PETE'S SAKE, KNOCK IT OFF! YOU GO AROUND THE HOUSE AND COUNT TO FIFTY, AND THEN WE BEGIN, ALL RIGHT?

YOU AND YOUR DUMB JAMS. THIS IS *WAR*, REMEMBER?!

YOU'RE JUST JEALOUS. ...OOH, WHAT A BABE!

28

CALVIN and HOBBES
by WATTERSON

CAN YOU BELIEVE THIS? SOME IDIOT TOSSED GARBAGE HERE IN THIS BEAUTIFUL SPOT.

I'LL BET FUTURE CIVILIZATIONS FIND OUT MORE ABOUT US THAN WE'D LIKE THEM TO KNOW.

LOOK, ANOTHER CAN THROWN ON THE GROUND! BOY, THIS MAKES ME MAD!

BY GOLLY, IF PEOPLE AREN'T BURYING TOXIC WASTES OR TESTING NUCLEAR WEAPONS, THEY'RE THROWING TRASH EVERYWHERE!

YOU'D THINK PLANETS LIKE THIS WERE A DIME A DOZEN! NOW *I'VE* GOT TO CARRY THIS GROSS THING.

YOU KNOW, THERE ARE TIMES WHEN IT'S A SOURCE OF PERSONAL PRIDE TO NOT BE HUMAN.

I'M WITH YOU.

YAWN

WAAUUGHH!

FOR THE LAST TIME, GET OUT OF BED! WE'RE GOING TO BE LATE.

I'M TRYING. I'M TRYING.

WATERSON

AREN'T THESE LONG SUMMER DAYS GREAT? NO RESPONSIBILITIES AT ALL! WE HAVE THE WHOLE DAY TO OURSELVES.

DON'T YOU WISH IT COULD BE LIKE THIS ALL YEAR, FOREVER? NO SCHOOL, NO JOB, NO ANYTHING?

!

YEAH, JUST GLOAT ABOUT IT, WHY DON'T YOU!!

WATERSON

HEY DAD, WHAT ARE CLOUDS MADE OF?

HMM... I USED TO KNOW THAT. I THINK THEY'RE MOSTLY WATER.

SO HOW COME THEY FLOAT?

WELL, IT'S SORT OF EVAPORATED WATER. MAYBE THERE ARE SOME OTHER GASES, TOO. I'M NOT SURE.

SO WHY ARE THEY WHITE WHEN THE REST OF THE SKY IS BLUE?

HECK, BEATS ME. I GUESS WE OUGHT TO LOOK THIS STUFF UP.

I TAKE IT THERE'S NO QUALIFYING EXAM TO BE A DAD.

ONE OF THE BEST THINGS ABOUT SUMMER IS GOING TO SLEEP WITH THE FAN ON.

THE GENTLE BREEZE BLOWING, THE DRONING HUM...EVERYTHING SEEMS SAFE AND SERENE WHEN THE FAN IS ON.

IT'S COOL AND LULLING AND PERFECT FOR SLEEP.

IT ALMOST LETS ONE FORGET HE HAS A HEAVY FUR COAT FOR A BUNKMATE.

IF YOU DON'T LIKE IT, THERE'S PLENTY OF ROOM ON THE FLOOR, BUSTER.

HEY MOM, WHAT'S THIS I HEAR ABOUT THE GREENHOUSE EFFECT?

THEY SAY THE POLLUTANTS WE DUMP IN THE AIR ARE TRAPPING IN THE SUN'S HEAT AND IT'S GOING TO MELT THE POLAR ICE CAPS!

SURE, *YOU'LL* BE GONE WHEN IT HAPPENS, BUT *I* WON'T! NICE PLANET YOU'RE LEAVING ME!

THIS FROM THE KID WHO WANTS TO BE CHAUFFEURED ANY PLACE MORE THAN A BLOCK AWAY.

HEY, NOBODY TOLD ME ABOUT THE ICE CAPS, ALL RIGHT?

MORE BAD NEWS ON YOUR POLLS, DAD. WE'RE LOOKING AT AN ALL-TIME LOW IN POPULARITY HERE.

WELL, CALVIN, THAT'S CERTAINLY FOOD FOR THOUGHT.

NOW HERE'S SOMETHING *YOU* CAN THINK ABOUT. THE AVERAGE COST OF RAISING A KID TO AGE 18 IS $100,000. THAT'S A LOT OF MONEY.

SO THE QUESTION YOU SHOULD BE ASKING YOURSELF IS, "IS THAT HUNDRED GRAND A *GIFT*... OR A *LOAN*?"

GOTCHA, DAD. I WAS JUST ON MY WAY TO BED.

HI THERE, CALVIN. I UNDERSTAND YOU'RE NOT FEELING WELL.

ME? I'M FINE! I JUST SIT AROUND TORTURE CHAMBERS IN MY UNDERWEAR FOR KICKS. LET'S SEE YOUR DEGREE, YOU QUACK!

I'M NOT GOING TO HURT YOU. I'M JUST GOING TO EXAMINE YOU TO SEE WHAT'S WRONG.

I'LL TELL YOU WHAT'S WRONG! I'VE GOT DR. FRANKENSTEIN FOR A PEDIATRICIAN, *THAT'S* WHAT'S WRONG!

NURSE, CALL THE ANESTHESIOLOGIST IN HERE, WILL YOU PLEASE?

MY DAD'S A LAWYER, I'LL HAVE YOU KNOW! DON'T COME NEAR ME!!

DEEP IN A DANK DUNGEON ON THE DISMAL PLANET ZOG, THE FEARLESS SPACEMAN SPIFF IS HELD PRISONER BY THE SINISTER ZOG KING.

A GUARD LEADS SPIFF TO THE INTERROGATION ROOM. OUR HERO IS STOIC AND DEFIANT!

AT LAST I MEET THE FAMED SPACEMAN SPIFF! I TRUST YOU ARE...HEH HEH... ENJOYING YOUR VISIT?

YOU'RE WASTING YOUR TIME, MAGGOT FROM MARS! I'LL NEVER GIVE IN!

NEVER, YOU HEAR ME?! *NEVER!*

KID, DON'T MAKE ME RECANT THE HIPPOCRATIC OATH, OK?

WELL, YOU CERTAINLY WERE A TERROR IN THE DOCTOR'S OFFICE.

I FENDED HIM OFF WITH HIS OWN TONGUE DEPRESSOR. THAT'S WHY I DIDN'T GET A SHOT.

YOU DIDN'T *NEED* A SHOT. YOUR BEHAVIOR WAS INEXCUSABLE.

ALL THAT COUNTS IS THAT HE COULDN'T GET NEAR ENOUGH TO STICK ME. HE THINKS I'M A LITTLE PINK PINCUSHION IN UNDERPANTS.

SOMEDAY I HOPE YOU HAVE A KID THAT PUTS YOU THROUGH WHAT I'VE GONE THROUGH.

YEAH, GRANDMA SAYS THAT'S WHAT SHE USED TO TELL *YOU*.

CalviN and HobbEs
by WATTERSON

THE FIRE'S NOT LIGHTING, HUH? CAN I MAKE A SUGGESTION?

GIVE UP ON THAT SISSY LIGHTER FLUID.

CAN'T WE COOK THE HAMBURGERS YET?

THE COALS AREN'T HOT ENOUGH.

BUT I'M HUNGRY! I WANT TO EAT *NOW!*

WELL, YOU'LL JUST HAVE TO WAIT.

YOU KNOW, CALVIN, SOMETIMES THE ANTICIPATION OF SOMETHING IS MORE FUN THAN THE THING ITSELF ONCE YOU GET IT.

HERE WE ARE, IT'S A BEAUTIFUL EVENING. IT'S NICE TO JUST SIT HERE AND LOOK AT THE TREES WHILE WE WAIT FOR THE COALS TO GET HOT, DON'T YOU THINK?

DINNER WILL BE OVER SOON, AND AFTERWARD WE'LL BE DISTRACTED WITH OTHER THINGS TO DO. BUT NOW WE HAVE A FEW MINUTES TO OURSELVES TO ENJOY THE EVENING.

THESE SUMMER DAYS GO BY SO QUICKLY. IT'S GOOD THAT EVERY NOW AND THEN WE HAVE TO WAIT FOR SOMETHING.

SO SHOULD I GO TO McDONALD'S THEN, OR WHAT?

YEAH, I KNOW. YOU THINK YOU'RE GOING TO BE SIX ALL YOUR LIFE.

HERE IS A PROUD CITY, FULL OF HAPPY, PROSPEROUS CITIZENS.

THEY GO ON ABOUT THEIR BUSINESS, **UNAWARE** THAT THE MOON HAS MYSTERIOUSLY MOVED A FEW MILES CLOSER TO THE EARTH.

...UNAWARE, THAT IS, UNTIL THE TIDE COMES IN.

SPLOOSH!

GISSHHH!

WHAT A PERFECT DAY!

ISN'T IT GREAT TO BE ON SUMMER VACATION? TO BE ABLE TO ENJOY ALL THIS WITH NO SCHOOL AND NO RESPONSIBILITIES?

..AHHHHHHHH...

I CAN'T BELIEVE THERE'S NOTHING ON TV BUT REPEATS.

DAD, CAN YOU GET MY BALL OUT OF THE GUTTER AGAIN?

THIS IS THE THIRD TIME THIS AFTERNOON! I THOUGHT I TOLD YOU TO PLAY OUT BACK!

RELAX, DAD. IT'S JUST A BALL IN THE GUTTER. IT'S NOT AS IF I'VE BEEN EMBEZZLING MONEY OR KILLING PEOPLE, RIGHT? AREN'T YOU GLAD I'M NOT STEALING AND MURDERING?

I ALWAYS HAVE TO HELP DAD ESTABLISH THE PROPER CONTEXT.

C'MON, HOBBES. LET DOWN THE ROPE LADDER.

WHAT'S THE REST OF THE PASSWORD?

I THINK FIVE VERSES EXTOLLING TIGERS IS *PLENTY*. YOU KNOW IT'S ME! LET ME UP!

NO.

OOH, WHY YOU 'LOUSY, ROTTEN, STINKING..

IF YOU CALL ME NAMES, YOU HAVE TO START OVER AT THE BEGINNING.

VERSE SIX: "TIGERS ARE NIMBLE AND LIGHT ON THEIR TOES, MY *RE*SPECT FOR TIGERS CONTINUALLY GROWS."

YOU'RE NOT DOING THE DANCE.

Calvin and Hobbes

by WATTERSON

THAT RUN DOESN'T COUNT! YOU DIDN'T TOUCH THIRD BASE!

THAT'S 'CAUSE THIRD BASE CRAWLED TO THE OUTFIELD!

WAP!

HA HA! EASY OUT!!

HEY! WHERE ARE YOU GOING?!

EEEEEE

YOU HAVE TO STAY ON THE BASE LINE, YOU CHEATER!

YEAH? PROVE IT!

THIS ISN'T FAIR! YOU CAN'T RUN ANYWHERE!

JUST WATCH ME!

IF WE HAD A FIRST BASEMAN, YOU'D'VE BEEN OUT LONG AGO!

BUT WE DON'T, DO WE?

GOTCHA! YOU'RE OUT!

OK, I'M UP TO BAT AGAIN! WHAT FUN! TWO-MAN BASEBALL IS A REAL SPORT!

A REAL SPORT FOR IDIOTS. NEXT TIME I'M GOING TO TAG YOU OUT WITH THE BAT INSTEAD OF THE BALL.

40

WHEN'S THIS RAIN GOING TO LET UP?

I DON'T KNOW, CALVIN.

HEY, CHEER UP, GANG! I PACKED STORM GEAR. "ALWAYS BE PREPARED," YOU KNOW.

THESE PONCHOS ARE SUPER. THEY'RE THERMAL-SEALED LIGHTWEIGHT NYLON, LAMINATED WITH FLEXIBLE URETHANE FOR COMPLETE WATER PROTECTION!

YEAH, DAD. IT'S GREAT THAT WE WON'T GET WETTER THAN WE ALREADY ARE.

ZINC OXIDE, THONGS, TANNING LOTION... WRONG DUFFEL BAG. LET'S SEE, WHICH ONE OF THESE WAS IT?

I'M GLAD DAD FINALLY GOT THE TENTS UP. NOW I CAN GET OUT OF THESE SOGGY CLOTHES.

TOO BAD *YOU* CAN'T PUT ON DRY CLOTHES. YOU'D FEEL A LOT BETTER.

HEY, WAIT! NO! DON'T DO THAT HERE!!

ACKPTH!

SOME TROUPER *YOU* ARE! WHAT'S A LITTLE RAIN? THIS IS WHAT BEING IN THE WILDERNESS IS ALL ABOUT!

HA HA! AT LEAST IT'S NOT *SNOWING*, RIGHT?

RIGHT?

I MEAN, SAY IT WAS SNOWING SO HARD WE COULDN'T MAKE A FIRE.

BOY, I LOVE COLD CANNED RAVIOLI.

TUM DE TA TA DEE DEE DO

BOY, THIS SURE BEATS SITTING IN AN OFFICE ALL DAY!

IS IT STILL RAINING?

OF COURSE IT'S STILL RAINING. IT'S BEEN RAINING FOR DAYS. WHY SHOULD IT STOP NOW?!

WE'RE GOING TO NEED A VACATION AFTER THIS VACATION.

I'LL SAY! WE CAN'T EVEN KEEP A FIRE GOING.

I CAN'T BELIEVE DAD WENT OUT TO CATCH FISH.

IN THIS WEATHER? HE'S A FANATIC!

EITHER THAT, OR WE'RE ALL OUT OF PACKAGED FOOD. WE'LL PROBABLY STARVE TO DEATH ON THIS GOD-FORSAKEN ROCK.

AFTER ALL THAT SPAM, STARVING DOESN'T SOUND SO BAD.

IF WE LIVE TO GET HOME, I'M NEVER GOING TO SET FOOT OUTSIDE AGAIN AS LONG AS I LIVE.

WHAT A LUCKY KID CALVIN IS! I NEVER GOT TO DO THIS STUFF WHEN I WAS HIS AGE!

HEY CALVIN! WANT TO LEARN HOW TO GUT A FISH?

WELL, GANG, I'M SORRY THE WEATHER WASN'T ANY BETTER THIS WEEK.

I KNOW IT WASN'T ALWAYS A LOT OF FUN, BUT WE LIVED THROUGH IT, AND WE GOT TO SPEND SOME TIME TOGETHER, AND THAT'S WHAT'S REALLY IMPORTANT.

ANYWAY, I HOPE YOU'RE ALL NOT *TOO* DISAPPOINTED.

CALVIN, TELL YOUR DAD ANY JUDGE WOULD TAKE THIS TRIP AS GROUNDS FOR DIVORCE.

DAD, MOM SAYS...

ALL RIGHT! ALL RIGHT!

THE END OF SUMMER IS ALWAYS HARD ON ME.

...TRYING TO CRAM IN ALL THE GOOFING OFF I'VE BEEN MEANING TO DO.

I DON'T *WANNA* TAKE A BATH! I *HATE* TAKING BATHS!

AAAAAAAAAAAAA

NO NO NO NO NO NO NO NO NO NO NO NO NO NO NO

THEY CAN MAKE ME DO IT, BUT THEY CAN'T MAKE ME DO IT WITH DIGNITY.

Calvin and Hobbes by WATTERSON

AH-CHOO!

WHEN ... NO BRAINS.

AH.. AH.. AH.. **AH**

CHOOO!

THE FORCE OF THE NASAL EXPLOSION SENDS CALVIN REELING THROUGH THE STRATOSPHERE!

WITH LESS AND LESS AIR TO RESIST HIS MOMENTUM, HE BREAKS THE PULL OF EARTH'S GRAVITY AND HURLS PAST THE MOON!

AS HE PASSES OUT OF THE GALAXY, CALVIN REFLECTS ON THE WISDOM OF COVERING ONE'S MOUTH WHEN SNEEZING TO DEFLECT THE PROPULSION.

ALAS, IT IS KNOWLEDGE GAINED TOO LATE FOR POOR CALVIN, THE HUMAN SATELLITE! ...BUT WAIT! ANOTHER SNEEZE IS BREWING! CALVIN TURNS HIMSELF AROUND!

THE SECOND SNEEZE ROCKETS HIM BACK TO EARTH! HE'S SAVED! IT'S A MIRACLE!

AH CHOO!

GOD BLESS YOU.

OH, HE *DOES*, MOM. HE *DOES*.

WATTERSON

46

WANT TO GO TIME TRAVELING WITH ME?

SEE, I BUILT A TIME MACHINE.

TIME MACHINE

THIS LOOKS LIKE YOUR TRANSMOGRIFIER.

TO THE INATTENTIVE AND BRAINLESS LAYMAN, YES. BUT YOU CRAWL **UNDER** THE TRANSMOGRIFIER, WHEREAS WITH THE TIME MACHINE, YOU CLIMB IN THE **TOP**.

AHH..

ARE WE GOING TO TRAVEL INTO THE PAST OR INTO THE FUTURE?

WELL, I SUPPOSE IF WE WENT INTO THE PAST, I COULD ACE ANY UPCOMING HISTORY EXAMS IN SCHOOL. THAT MIGHT BE USEFUL.

BUT IF WE WENT INTO THE FUTURE, WE COULD SWIPE SOMETHING AND PRETEND TO INVENT IT WHEN WE GOT BACK. WE COULD BE RICH.

THE FUTURE IT IS, THEN!

RIGHT. ONCE I'M RICH, I CAN *HIRE* SOMEBODY TO TAKE ALL MY DUMB TESTS!

TIME MACHINE

OK, HOBBES, OUR TIME MACHINE IS ALL SET. PUT ON YOUR GOGGLES AND WE'LL BE OFF TO THE FUTURE!

TIME MACHINE

WHY DO WE HAVE TO WEAR GOGGLES?

GEEZ, DO YOU THINK TRAVELING YEARS INTO THE FUTURE IS LIKE DRIVING DOWN THE STREET?!

WE'VE GOT TO CONTEND WITH VORTEXES AND LIGHT SPEEDS! ANYTHING COULD GO WRONG! OF COURSE WE NEED TO WEAR GOGGLES!

GOSH, I THINK MY GOGGLES ARE IN THE BEDROOM. IF I'M NOT BACK IN A COUPLE MINUTES, YOU CAN GO WITHOUT ME.

SIT DOWN, SISSY. I ALREADY GOT YOUR GOGGLES.

TIME MACHINE

WE MADE IT! IT'S A GOOD THING THE TIME MACHINE DIDN'T STALL, OR WE'D HAVE BEEN EATEN BY DINOSAURS!

WE'RE COMING BACK TOWARD THE PRESENT NOW. DO YOU WANT TO STOP AT HOME, OR KEEP GOING INTO THE FUTURE LIKE WE PLANNED?

I'VE HAD ENOUGH TIME TRAVELING. LET'S GO HOME.

LET'S GO JUST A *LITTLE* INTO THE FUTURE AND SEE WHAT I'M LIKE AS A TEEN-AGER!

LET'S NOT, ALL RIGHT?

HI, MOM. HOBBES AND I WENT TIME TRAVELING AND VISITED THE JURASSIC PERIOD TODAY.

THAT'S NICE. WHAT'S IT LIKE?

PRETTY SCARY. A DINOSAUR ALMOST ATE US.

ACTUALLY, WE WERE TRYING TO GO INTO THE FUTURE, BUT WE MADE A MISTAKE.

I SEE. WELL, I'M GLAD YOU MADE IT BACK.

YOUR MOM ISN'T FAZED BY MUCH, IS SHE?

IT DEPENDS. SHE DIDN'T TAKE THE FROGS IN THE TOILET SO WELL, REMEMBER?

HOW COME YOU'RE STILL HOME? WHY AREN'T YOU AT WORK?

I TOOK THE DAY OFF.

SAY, DAD, CAN I HAVE A LOOK AT THE CLASSIFIED SECTION?

AS SOON AS I'M THROUGH WITH IT.

GOSH, DAD, I'D SURE LIKE TO BORROW THAT SECTION RIGHT THIS MINUTE. WHY DON'T YOU READ THE EDITORIALS?

"NEW DAD WANTED. FREQUENT TRAVELER PREFERRED. LIBERAL VIEWS ON DISCIPLINE A MUST. ASK FOR CALVIN DURING NORMAL WORK HOURS."

BU·URRP!

GOOD HEAVENS, CALVIN! WHAT DO WE SAY AFTER THAT?

"MUST BE A BARGE COMING THROUGH!"

WHAT DO YOU SAY?!

"THAT SURE TASTED BETTER GOING DOWN THAN COMING UP!"

THREE STRIKES AND YOU'RE HISTORY, KIDDO.

EXCUSE ME.

DAD, LOOK! THE SUN'S SETTING AND ITS ONLY 3 O'CLOCK!

IT'S NOT 3 O'CLOCK. YOUR WATCH STOPPED.

TIME DOESN'T STOP IF YOUR WATCH STOPS?

NOPE.

PHOOEY. FOR A MOMENT THERE, I THOUGHT I'D GET RICH PATENTING THIS THING.

I'D HAVE BOUGHT ONE.

calvin and hobbes

by WATTERSON

STIR STIR

STRETTCCHHH

STAB STAB

PAT PAT PAT

MUSH MUSH

SNIFF

HWOOF!

LICK

NCKPTGH

BLECHH

GLUG GLUG GLUG

SMACK

BR-R-R-R-R

HAAAKK HOCCHH

CHOKE... GASP...

THERE... (PANT)... SEE? I...I... *TRIED* IT. (COUGH) IT... ALMOST (WHEEZE) KILLED... ME.

CLAP CLAP CLAP CLAP CL

ENCORE. BRA*VO.*

I'M GOING TO RUN AWAY TO ALASKA.

54

WELL, I GUESS WE'RE ALL PACKED. COMIC BOOKS, DART GUN, SPACE HELMET AND TOBOGGAN! WE'RE OFF TO THE YUKON!

DO WE HAVE A MAP?

OOH, THAT'S RIGHT! GLAD YOU REMEMBERED! I'LL GO GET ONE!

DON'T WE HAVE ANY ROAD MAPS OF THE YUKON, MOM?

I DOUBT IT.

OK, HERE'S THE YUKON. NOW SEE IF YOU CAN FIND THE UNITED STATES.

HERE THEY ARE! LOOK HOW CLOSE IT IS! THIS WON'T TAKE ANY TIME AT ALL!

SO LONG, "MOM"! WE'RE OFF TO THE YUKON. IT'S BEEN NICE LIVING HERE ... BUT NOT *REAL* NICE! HA HA!

CALVIN! WAIT A MINUTE.

LEAVE IT TO A MOTHER TO DRAG OUT A GOODBYE. SHEESH.

YOU'RE GOING SOUTHEAST. NORTH IS *THAT* WAY.

OH YEAH. I KNEW THAT.

THIS SLED IS HEAVY. I THOUGHT WE WERE GOING TO *RIDE* IT MOST OF THE WAY TO THE YUKON.

WE'VE ONLY BEEN WALKING 20 MINUTES, HOBBES. WE PROBABLY WON'T GET TO NORTHERN CANADA UNTIL THIS AFTERNOON.

IN THAT CASE, I'M TAKING A BREAK.

GOOD IDEA. WANT A COMIC BOOK? HERE'S CAPTAIN NITRO.

I WANT A SANDWICH.

WE JUST HAVE ONE APIECE. WE SHOULD SAVE 'EM IN CASE WE CAN'T CATCH A WALRUS.

GOSH, MAYBE MOM AND DAD SOLD ALL MY BELONGINGS WHEN I SECEDED.

MAYBE THEY RENTED OUT MY ROOM.

MAYBE THEY *MOVED!*

...A LOT CAN HAPPEN WHEN YOU'RE GONE ALL MORNING!

...MOMMMM!!

I'M BACK, MOM. I CHANGED MY MIND ABOUT SECEDING. I WANT TO BE YOUR KID AGAIN, OK?

YOU'LL ALWAYS BE MY KID. I'M GLAD YOU'RE BACK.

WELL, HOBBES WAS BEING A MORON, SO I DECIDED I DIDN'T WANT TO LIVE IN THE YUKON WITH HIM.

SO WHERE IS HOBBES NOW?

ISN'T HE BACK YET?

HOW COULD HOBBES GET BACK BY HIMSELF?!

YOU'RE RIGHT. THAT DUMB TIGER COULDN'T FIND HIS WAY OUT OF AN EMPTY ROOM.

BEDTIME, CALVIN.

WHERE'S HOBBES?

I SUPPOSE HE'S WHEREVER YOU LEFT HIM.

YOU MEAN HE'S STILL IN THE WOODS?! IT'S NIGHT OUT!

WHAT HAVE I TOLD YOU ABOUT LEAVING YOUR BELONGINGS?

HOBBES IS LOST! I'LL GET A FLASHLIGHT! WE'VE GOT TO FIND HIM!

HOBBES! HOBBES!

CALVIN, IT'S YOUR BEDTIME! DON'T YOU PULL THIS STUNT *NOW!*

Calvin and Hobbes by WATTERSON

HOBBES, YOU MANGY FUZZ-BRAINED LUNKHEAD, WHERE ARE YOU??

...I DIDN'T MEAN THAT QUITE THE WAY THAT SOUNDED.

C'MON, CALVIN, GET BACK INSIDE. IT'S TOO LATE TO GO SEARCHING FOR YOUR STUFFED TIGER NOW.

I CAN'T LEAVE HOBBES ALONE IN THE WOODS AT NIGHT!

WELL, MAYBE YOU SHOULD HAVE THOUGHT ABOUT THAT BEFORE IT GOT DARK. THIS CAN BE A LITTLE LESSON, HMM?

I THOUGHT HE'D COME BACK BY HIMSELF. I DIDN'T THINK HE'D GET *LOST!*

WE'LL LOOK FOR HIM TOMORROW. NOW OFF TO BED WITH YOU.

(SNIFF) I HOPE HE'S OK. IF HE HADN'T BEEN ACTING SO STUPID I NEVER WOULD'VE LEFT HIM.

I SURE WISH HE'D COME BACK.

CALVIN LEFT HOBBES SOMEWHERE IN THE WOODS. THE POOR KID'S PRETTY UPSET.

I'LL BET.

I MEAN, HE'S *REALLY* UPSET.

I SAID I'LL BET HE IS.

REALLY UPSET.

...AHH...

WOULD *MY* DAD HAVE DONE THIS? OF COURSE NOT. *I* WAS NEVER SPOILED LIKE THIS...

Calvin and Hobbes

by WATTERSON

WIPE THAT GRIN OFF YOUR FACE!

WELL, HOBBES, HOW DO I LOOK?

I'M DOING MY BEST TO BITE MY TONGUE.

I CUT OUT CONSTRUCTION PAPER FEATHERS AND TAPED THEM ON MY ARMS SO I CAN FLY! PRETTY NEAT, HUH?

IF PAPER FEATHERS ARE ALL IT TAKES TO FLY, DON'T YOU THINK WE'D HAVE HEARD ABOUT IT BEFORE?

IT TAKES AN UNCOMMON MIND TO THINK OF THESE THINGS, HOBBES.

I'D AGREE WITH THAT.

HERE'S A GORGE. THIS IS A GOOD SPOT.

YOU'RE GOING TO JUMP OFF THIS LEDGE?

HECK NO! I NEED *MOMENTUM*! I WANT YOU TO *TOSS* ME OVER.

YOU UNDERSTAND I ASSUME NO RESPONSIBILITY FOR THIS?

RIGHT. *I* GET THE PATENT.

HEAVE!

I'M FLYING! I'M FLYING!

I'M..... UH OH...

DON'T SELL THE BIKE SHOP, ORVILLE.

SHUT UP AND GO GET ME SOME ANTISEPTIC.

WATTERSON

LET'S SEE WHAT YOU DREW FOR ART CLASS, SUSIE.

WELL, A TIDY LITTLE DOMESTIC SCENE. A HOUSE IN A YARD WITH FLOWERS. HOW TYPICALLY FEMALE.

GIRLS THINK SMALL AND ARE PREOCCUPIED WITH PETTY DETAILS. BUT *BOYS* THINK *BIG!* BOYS THINK ABOUT ACTION AND ACCOMPLISHMENT! NO WONDER IT'S *MEN* WHO CHANGE THE WORLD!

YEAH? WHAT DID *YOU* DRAW?

A SQUADRON OF B-1s NUKING NEW YORK.

UH-OH, IT HAPPENED AGAIN.

CALVIN WAKES UP WITHOUT ANY RECOGNIZABLE FEATURES, SAVE TWO ANTENNAE. HOW DISGUSTING.

HE OOZES OUT OF BED ON A TRAIL OF SLIME. LACKING ARMS AND LEGS, HOW WILL CALVIN PUT ON HIS CLOTHES?

AREN'T YOU DRESSED YET? YOU ARE SO SLUGGISH IN THE MORNING!

WHERE ARE YOU GOING WITH THE TOY TELEPHONE?

OUT IN THE WOODS. YOU CAN COME ALONG IF YOU'D LIKE.

WHAT ARE YOU GOING TO DO?

TRY SOME BIRD CALLS.

CALVIN and HOBBES

by WATTERSON

YOUR DAD AND I ARE GOING OUT TO SEE A MOVIE TONIGHT.

CAN I COME TOO?

NO, YOU'RE STAYING HOME.

WHAT, I GOT THE PLAGUE?! WHY CAN'T I COME?

BECAUSE OTHER PEOPLE LIKE TO WATCH MOVIES WITHOUT HEARING ADVICE SHOUTED TO THE CHARACTERS ON THE SCREEN.

SO WHO DOES *THAT*? ARE YOU SAYING *I* DO THAT?

MOM WON'T LET US GO TO THE MOVIE WITH THEM, SO I GUESS WE'RE ON OUR OWN TONIGHT.

CAN WE WATCH TV?

WHAT MOM AND DAD DON'T KNOW WON'T HURT 'EM, RIGHT?

IN FACT, AFTER THEY LEAVE, LET'S GET IN THE OTHER CAR AND LEARN TO DRIVE!

OH BOY! I GET TO BEEP THE HORN, OK?

HEY, THERE'S A TEEN-AGER COMING UP THE DRIVE. OH NO! IT'S *ROSALYN!*

OUR BABY SITTER?! WHAT'S SHE DOING HERE? DON'T MOM AND DAD *TRUST* US?? QUICK, HIDE!!

WE'RE LEAVING NOW, ROSALYN. CALVIN IS UPSTAIRS.

I HOPE HE'S NOT TOO MUCH TROUBLE TONIGHT.

DON'T WORRY, I BROUGHT A CATTLE PROD THIS TIME!

YOUR MOM AND DAD LAUGHED. MAYBE IT WAS A JOKE.

MAYBE MOM AND DAD THINK SCORCHING LITTLE KIDS IS FUNNY. LET'S GO.

CALVIN? ARE YOU IN THERE? C'MON OUT AND WE'LL MAKE SOME POPCORN.

CALVIN? ...OH BROTHER...

I SEE YOU, CALVIN! C'MON BACK INSIDE!

NO WAY, LADY! IF YOU WANT US, YOU'LL HAVE TO CATCH US!

OH GEEZ, RUN!! SHE'S WEARING CLEATS!

OUTTA MY WAY! OUTTA MY WAY!

LET'S GO! BACK IN THE HOUSE! NO MORE MONKEY BUSINESS, ALL RIGHT?

PHOOEY.

IT'S MY JOB TO WATCH YOU AND THAT'S WHAT I'M GOING TO DO, EVEN IF I HAVE TO STRAP YOU TO A CHAIR.

GOT IT?

JAWOHL, MEIN FÜHRER!

CARE TO REPEAT THAT LITTLE COMMENT?

I SAID I'M NOT GOING ANYWHERE. LEGGO.

WE'RE HOME, ROSALYN. WAS CALVIN ANY TROUBLE?

NOT TOO MUCH. I SENT HIM TO BED A LITTLE WHILE AGO.

THAT'S GOOD.

KNOCK KNOCK

NOW WHO COULD THAT BE AT THIS HOUR?

POLICE, SIR. WE RECEIVED A CALL ABOUT TWO HOSTAGES BEING HELD HERE.

CALVIN! GET DOWN HERE!!

CALVIN and HOBBES by WATTERSON

PANT WHEEZE GASP

WELL, IF YOU DIDN'T GET IN A FIGHT AT SCHOOL, WHAT ON EARTH HAPPENED TO YOU?!

LET'S JUST SAY SOMETIMES I WISH I HAD A GERBIL.

HI, DAD. I'M REPEATING EVERYTHING ANYONE SAYS.

OH, YOU ARE, ARE YOU?

OH, YOU ARE, ARE YOU?

KNOCK IT OFF, CALVIN. THAT'S VERY ANNOYING.

KNOCK IT OFF, CALVIN. THAT'S VERY ANNOYING.

I FORFEIT ALL MY DESSERTS FOR A WEEK.

OK, GIVE THEM TO *ME*.

HA HA. WHY DON'T YOU GO BOTHER YOUR MOTHER FOR A WHILE?

PSST...SUSIE! WHAT'S THE ANSWER TO QUESTION FOUR?

IMADOOFUS.

THANKS!

THE TOOTH FAIRY'S GONNA MAKE YOU RICH TONIGHT, SUSIE.

HI, CALVIN. I BROUGHT MR. BUN OVER SO WE CAN PLAY HOUSE. YOU AND I CAN BE THE PARENTS, AND HOBBES AND MR. BUN CAN BE OUR CHILDREN.

OH, RIGHT. HOBBES AND I ARE GONNA PUT OUR BIG PLANS ON HOLD SO WE CAN PLAY HOUSE WITH A STUFFED RABBIT? FORGET IT!

I DON'T SEE WHY YOU'LL PLAY WITH YOUR DUMB OL' TIGER AND NOT WITH MR. BUN AND ME! YOU'RE JUST MEAN, THAT'S ALL!

GO PLAY IN A MICROWAVE, SUSIE. WE'RE BUSY.

GIRLS ARE LIKE SLUGS—THEY PROBABLY SERVE SOME PURPOSE, BUT IT'S HARD TO IMAGINE WHAT.

MR. BUN SEEMS COMATOSE. DID YOU NOTICE?

MOM, CAN HOBBES AND I RENT A VCR AND A TAPE TONIGHT?

I DON'T THINK SO, CALVIN. IT'S A SCHOOL NIGHT.

WHAT IF WE GOT AN *EDUCATIONAL* TAPE?

LIKE WHAT?

"CANNIBAL STEWARDESS VIXENS UNCHAINED."

NOW SHE WON'T EVEN LET US GO INTO THE *STORE.*

I THINK WE'D LEARN A *LOT* BY WATCHING THAT.

NOBODY HAD BETTER BE SNEAKING UP ON ME!!

WHUMP!

IT'S HARD TO CHANGE DIRECTION IN MID-AIR.

BUDDY, I'M GOING TO CHANGE A LOT MORE THAN YOUR DIRECTION.

Girl: HEY, CALVIN, WHY'D YOU BRING YOUR STUFFED TIGER TO SCHOOL? IT'S NOT A SHOW-AND-TELL DAY.

Calvin: I KNOW. HOBBES IS GOING TO GIVE MOE A LITTLE "TREAT" TODAY: A RIDE IN AN AMBULANCE HELICOPTER.

Girl: YEAH? HOW'S HE GOING TO DO *THAT*?

Calvin: IF YOU HAVE AN AVERSION TO DESCRIPTIONS OF CARNAGE, YOU PROBABLY DON'T WANT TO KNOW.

Girl: TALKING WITH YOU IS SORT OF THE CONVERSATIONAL EQUIVALENT OF AN OUT-OF-BODY EXPERIENCE.

Calvin: DON'T GET TOO CLOSE NOW. I WANT HOBBES TO STAY FRESH FOR THIS AFTERNOON.

Moe: Look, Calvin's got a teddy bear. That's real sweet, Cal.

Calvin: IT'S A TIGER, YOU BRAINLESS INVERTEBRATE.

Moe: Hey, maybe I'd like to play with your teddy!

Calvin: GOOD IDEA, MOE. HOBBES PLAYS KINDA ROUGH, BUT HE'S *LOTS* OF FUN. C'MERE AND TAKE HIM.

Moe: Why? Is the teacher watching? This is a trick, right? I'm not touching your stupid teddy, see?

Calvin: C'MON, I DARE YOU! WHAT'S THE MATTER? ARE YOU CHICKEN?

Calvin: HA HA! BOY, YOU SURE SCARED *HIM* OFF! YOU WERE GREAT!

Hobbes: COME BACK AND CALL ME A "BEAR" AGAIN! YEAH, *YOU*, BUB!!

Calvin: I CALLED YOUR TEACHER ABOUT MOE'S BULLYING, AND SHE SAID SHE'D PUT A STOP TO IT.

Calvin: I'M AFRAID YOU WASTED YOUR TIME, MOM. MOE TOOK ONE LOOK AT HOBBES AND JUST ABOUT LOST HIS LUNCH!

Calvin: I DON'T THINK MOE WILL BE BOTHERING *ME* FOR A WHILE. IT'S NOT EVERY KID WHO HAS A *TIGER* FOR A BEST FRIEND.

Calvin: ...AND WHAT LUCKY MOMS THOSE OTHER KIDS HAVE.

Mom: C'MON, HOBBES, IF YOU'LL LEND ME A BUCK, I'LL BUY YOU A COMIC BOOK.

SNIP SNAP CRACK

SHICKA SHICKA WWHISSSHHH

F SHOOF SHOOF SHOOF SHOO

KRITCH KRUNCH KRITCH KRUNCH

SOMETIMES IT'S GOOD TO HUSH UP AWHILE AND LET AUTUMN STICK IN A FEW WORDS.

PROCESSED LUNCH MEAT IS PRETTY SCARY. WHAT *ARE* THESE LITTLE SPECKS, ANYWAY? LIZARD PARTS? WHO KNOWS?

AND THIS "SKIN"! I HEARD IT USED TO BE MADE OF INTESTINE, BUT I THINK NOWADAYS IT'S PLASTIC.

OF COURSE, THEY DYE AND WAX FRUIT SO IT LOOKS BETTER. IT'S LIKE EATING A CANDLE.

AND MOM WONDERS WHY I'M SO HUNGRY AFTER SCHOOL.

YEP, WE'D PROBABLY BE DEAD NOW IF IT WASN'T FOR TWINKIES.

WITH ULTRASONIC HEARING, *STUPENDOUS MAN* NOTICES A CRY OF DISTRESS FROM A DISTANT ALLEYWAY!

HE LEAPS TO THE EDGE OF THE BUILDING AND PREPARES TO SWOOP TO THE RESCUE!

STUPENDOUS MAN HAD NOT QUITE REALIZED JUST HOW HIGH UP HE WAS, HOWEVER. AT THIS ALTITUDE THE WINDS WERE A LITTLE TRICKY, AND...

ARE YOU GOING, OR DO YOU NEED A PUSH?

DON'T RUSH ME, ALL RIGHT?!

ACK! ICK!

ACKPT! GHK!

HA-HA HA HA BLECHTH GAKCK

LURCH YOUR WAY TO THE CAR, KID. YOU NEED A HAIRCUT.

THINK IT'S GETTING ANY COLDER OUT?

NOT REALLY.

I DON'T THINK IT'S GONNA CHANGE.

ME EITHER.

NUTS. WELL, LET'S GO IN.

75

STIR
STIR
STIR

STIR
STIR
STIR

I WON'T EAT ANY CEREAL THAT DOESN'T TURN THE MILK PURPLE.

THE DEADLY TORNADO MAKES ITS WAY ACROSS THE COMMUNITY!

THE CIRCLING UPDRAFT CLOCKS AT OVER 200 MPH! THE TWISTER SEARCHES FOR A TRAILER PARK!

FINDING ONE, IT TOUCHES DOWN! DEBRIS IS THROWN FOR MILES IN THE ENSUING EXPLOSION OF RUSHING AIR!

WHEN ARE YOU GOING TO CLEAN UP THIS ROOM?! IT LOOKS LIKE A...

TORNADO HIT IT, I KNOW.

OH BOY, IT'S SATURDAY!!

WHAT'S GOING ON? WHY AREN'T THERE ANY CARTOONS ON TV? IT'S JUST A TEST PATTERN.

THE TV GUIDE SAYS THEY DON'T START UNTIL 6:30.

HECK, THAT'S 45 MINUTES FROM NOW! WELL, C'MON, I'LL RACE YOU UP AND DOWN THE STAIRS!

WHY CAN'T HE EVER GET UP LIKE THIS ON SCHOOL DAYS?

GO BREAK HIS LITTLE LEGS, WILL YOU, HONEY?

BANG!
BONK

BAD NEWS ON YOUR CAMPAIGN TO STAY DAD, DAD.

OH?

YEP. THE LATEST POLL OF SIX-YEAR-OLDS IN THIS HOUSEHOLD SHOWS THAT THEY DON'T CARE ABOUT ISSUES THIS YEAR. IT'S CHARACTER THAT COUNTS.

SO WHY IS THAT BAD NEWS?

WHO'S THE BIMBO WITH YOU IN THIS OLD PROM PICTURE?

THAT "BIMBO" IS YOUR MOTHER!

WHO'S A BIMBO??

PRETTY FUNKY HAIRDO, MOM!

IT'S THE SAD TRUTH, DAD. NOBODY CARES ABOUT YOUR POSITIONS ON FATHERHOOD. WE JUST WANT TO KNOW ABOUT YOUR CHARACTER.

IF YOU'RE GOING TO BE DAD HERE, WE HAVE TO KNOW YOU'VE NEVER DONE OR SAID ANYTHING THAT WOULD REFLECT POORLY ON YOUR JUDGMENT.

I HAVE YOUR COLLEGE YEARBOOK HERE. LET'S FLIP THROUGH IT, SHALL WE?

IS THIS YOU WITH THE KEG AND THE "PARTY NAKED" T-SHIRT?

GIVE ME THAAAT!

GRANDPA SAYS THE COMICS WERE A LOT BETTER YEARS AGO WHEN NEWSPAPERS PRINTED THEM BIGGER.

HE SAYS COMICS NOW ARE JUST A BUNCH OF XEROXED TALKING HEADS BECAUSE THERE'S NO SPACE TO TELL A DECENT STORY OR TO SHOW ANY ACTION.

HE THINKS PEOPLE SHOULD WRITE TO THEIR NEWSPAPERS AND COMPLAIN.

YOUR GRANDPA TAKES THE FUNNIES PRETTY SERIOUSLY.

YEAH, MOM'S LOOKING INTO NURSING HOMES.

calvin and HOBBES
by WATTERSON

KISS HOBBES GOOD NIGHT TOO, MOM.

IF YOU DON'T GET A GOOD NIGHT KISS, YOU GET KAFKA DREAMS.

SLEEP TIGHT. "DON'T LET THE BEDBUGS BITE."

WHAT'S *THAT* SUPPOSED TO MEAN? DO WE HAVE VERMIN IN THIS HOUSE??

THE MATTRESS IS MOVING!

WHOA! IT MUST BE A BEDBUG!

GAAH! LEGS!! IT MUST BE HUGE! HOW DISGUSTING! UGGHH!!

I'LL RUN FOR SOME BUG SPRAY! DON'T LET HIM OUT!

I NEED MORE WEIGHT! PUT YOUR FOOT LOCKER UP HERE!

WHAT'S GOING *ON* UP THERE?!

IT SOUNDS LIKE HE'S MOVING *FURNITURE!*

I GOT SOME RAID! LIFT UP THE MATTRESS!

LET HIM HAVE IT!

GOSH, ALL THAT SPRAY DIDN'T KILL HIM! WHAT ARE WE GONNA DO?!

I HEAR YOUR DAD COMING! MAYBE *HE* CAN KILL IT!

ABOUT TIME, DAD! HE CRAWLED BACK INTO THE BED! GET A FLY SWATTER!

I'LL (COUGH) TELL YOU WHO'S GOING TO GET SWATTED! (CHOKE) WHAT HAVE YOU DONE TO THIS ROOM?!!

DID YOU READ THIS? THIS TV STAR MADE OVER TWENTY MILLION DOLLARS LAST YEAR!

WHAT WOULD *YOU* DO WITH TWENTY MILLION BUCKS?

BEATS ME. I THINK IT'S RIDICULOUS THAT ANYONE MAKES THAT KIND OF MONEY.

OK, SAY YOU ONLY MADE *FIFTEEN* MILLION.

LET'S SAY EIGHTEEN.

HI, MOM.

BUM BA DA BUM BUM

WHAT'S COOKING?

HA HA HA HA HA HA!

WHAT'S WITH *YOU*?

I THOUGHT MY LIFE WOULD SEEM MORE INTERESTING WITH A MUSICAL SCORE AND A LAUGH TRACK.

I MADE UP A JOKE. A MAN'S GOING FOR A WALK, SO HE GETS HIS DOG AND SAYS, "HEEL!"

..AND THE DOG LOOKS UP AND SAYS, "IT TAKES ONE TO KNOW ONE, BUSTER!" HA HA HA HA HA!!

WHAT'S THE MATTER WITH YOU? DON'T YOU *GET* IT?!

AHHH, WHAT DO TIGERS KNOW ABOUT SOPHISTICATED HUMOR, ANYWAY?

HOW DID THE DOG LEARN TO TALK?

WHATCHA DOIN'? COUNTERFEITING MONEY.

IT'S REALLY HARD. LOOK AT ALL THE LITTLE LINES ON THIS BILL.

THINK ANYONE WILL FALL FOR YOUR FORGERY? SURE. EVERYONE WILL.

OL' GEORGE HAS THE GOUT, I SEE. I *SAID* THIS WAS HARD.

THE GIANT WHALE SWIMS TOWARD THE SURFACE!

ITS MASSIVE TAIL PUMPING FURIOUSLY, HE GAINS TERRIFYING MOMENTUM!

THE 35-TON BEHEMOTH BREACHES! HE CRASHES INTO THE SURF WITH DEAFENING IMPACT!

CALVIN, YOU'D BETTER NOT BE SPLASHING THE FLOOR, YOU HEAR ME?! YAAAH

QUIT HOGGING THE BED. YOU'RE WAY OVER ON MY SIDE.

TOUGH BEANS, FUZZ FACE.

EVER THINK ABOUT GEYSERS AND WATERFALLS? HUNDREDS OF THOUSANDS OF GALLONS OF WATER! FLOWING, SPILLING, RUSHING, GUSHING, SPLASHING!

HE REALLY FIGHTS MEAN.

SPACEMAN SPIFF FLEES THE DESPICABLE SCUM BEINGS OF PLANET Q-13!

IN A SURPRISE MANEUVER, OUR HERO TURNS TO FACE THE ADVERSARY! HIS HAND TIGHTENS AROUND THE DEATH RAY TRIGGER!

IT DOESN'T RESPOND! SPIFF REACHES FOR THE MERTILIZER BEAM, BUT IT DOESN'T WORK EITHER! NEITHER DO THE PHOSPHO BOMBS OR THE MORDO BLASTERS! NOTHING IS WORKING!!

1812! GETTYSBURG! 16 FLUID OUNCES! I BEFORE E! THOMAS EDISON!

PERHAPS SOMEONE WHO HAS BEEN *PAYING ATTENTION* CAN HELP OUT CALVIN?

z

YAAHH!

z

I KEEP FORGETTING THAT FIVE OF HIS SIX ENDS ARE POINTY WHEN HE LIES LIKE THAT.

SINCE SEPTEMBER, IT'S JUST GOTTEN COLDER AND COLDER.

THERE'S LESS DAYLIGHT NOW, I'VE NOTICED, TOO.

OH NO! THIS CAN ONLY MEAN ONE THING!

THE SUN IS GOING OUT! IN A FEW MORE MONTHS EARTH WILL BE A DARK AND LIFELESS BALL OF ICE!

WELL, GEE, NOW I DON'T FEEL SO BAD ABOUT NOT SETTING UP AN IRA LAST YEAR.

DAD SAYS THE SUN ISN'T GOING OUT.

HE SAYS IT'S COLDER BECAUSE OUR HEMISPHERE IS TILTED AWAY FROM THE SUN NOW.

HE SAYS WINTER WILL BE HERE SOON.

ISN'T IT SAD HOW SOME PEOPLE'S GRIP ON THEIR LIVES IS SO PRECARIOUS THAT THEY'LL EMBRACE ANY PREPOSTEROUS DELUSION RATHER THAN FACE AN OCCASIONAL BLEAK TRUTH?

ARE YOU GOING TO LIVE THE LAST FEW MONTHS OF YOUR LIFE ANY DIFFERENTLY, NOW THAT THE SUN IS GOING OUT AND WE'RE ALL DOOMED?

NO, I'VE ALWAYS BELIEVED IN LIVING EACH DAY AS IF IT WAS MY LAST, SO I NEVER HAVE ANY REGRETS.

KIND OF INSPIRING, HUH?

IF YOU WERE SOMEONE ELSE, IT MIGHT BE.

PASS ME THAT ISSUE OF CAPTAIN NAPALM WILL YOU?

MY TEACHER SAID THE SAME THING DAD DID. THE SUN *ISN'T* GOING OUT AFTER ALL!

IT'S JUST GETTING COLDER BECAUSE WINTER'S COMING. DAD WAS RIGHT ALL ALONG!

IMAGINE OL' DAD KNOWING SOMETHING LIKE THAT!

WHAT'S THIS STORY YOU'RE GOING TO READ ME, DAD? IT DOESN'T HAVE ANY ROMANCE IN IT, DOES IT?

UH...

EDIT IT OUT IF IT DOES. I HATE ROMANCE. DOES IT HAVE ANY BORING DESCRIPTION IN IT?

WELL...

SKIP IT IF YOU SEE ANY. I LIKE MY STORIES FAST AND GRIPPING.

IT DOESN'T HAVE A MORAL, DOES IT? I HATE BEING TOLD HOW TO LIVE MY LIFE. SKIP THE MORAL, TOO, OK?

DOES HIS MAJESTY PREFER COLOR PICTURES, OR BLACK AND WHITE?

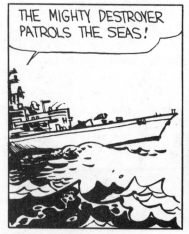

THE MIGHTY DESTROYER PATROLS THE SEAS!

SUDDENLY THE SHIP SPINS OUT OF CONTROL! IT'S CAUGHT IN A WHIRLPOOL!

WITHIN MOMENTS THE GIANT VESSEL DIPS ITS HULL INTO THE SWIRLING VORTEX AND IS NEVER SEEN AGAIN!

OH NO! HERE GOES THE REST OF THE NAVY!

ARE YOU LETTING THE WATER OUT *ALREADY?*

Calvin and Hobbes

by WATTERSON

CALVIN, IT'S TIME TO WAKE UP.

CALVIN, IT'S TIME TO WAKE UP.

C'MON, YOU'LL BE LATE FOR SCHOOL.

MY DREAMS ARE GETTING WAY TOO LITERAL.

I ALWAYS WANTED TO BE A CUB SCOUT AND GET MERIT BADGES AND STUFF, BUT I HATE GOING TO MEETINGS.

OK OK, JUST READ ABOUT KNOTS, ALL RIGHT?

HEY, LOOK, HERE'S A MOTTO! I DIDN'T KNOW YOU HAD A MOTTO! WOW, WHAT FUN!

"LIVE FOR REVENGE" IS GOING TO BE MY MOTTO IF YOU DON'T GET ME OUT OF THIS.

I'LL QUIZ YOU. WHAT DO YOU DO FOR A SECOND-DEGREE BURN?

DON'T FLIP THROUGH THE BOOK, YOU IDIOT! UNTIE ME!

HMPH, IF I WAS IN YOUR PREDICAMENT, I'D TREAT ME WITH A LOT MORE RESPECT. DO YOU SAY YOU'RE SORRY?

MMFF RRGGH! OOH! ARGH! YOU DIRTY ROTTEN STINKING

HOBBES, I'M NOT KIDDING. IF YOU DON'T GET ME LOOSE IN TEN SECONDS...

YOU GOT YOURSELF INTO THIS, "MR. HOUDINI," NOT ME.

BUT I'M SUPPOSED TO BE AT DINNER! MOM'S GONNA KILL ME!

ESCAPE ARTISTS HAVE A RISKY TRADE. HEY, HERE'S MORSE CODE!

OK, I'M SORRY I CALLED YOU NAMES. I SAID I'M SORRY, RIGHT? NOW UNTIE ME!

HERE'S HOW YOU SAY "BANANA" IN MORSE. DASH DOT DOT DOT, DOT DASH...

WHAT IS THAT KID DOING?! IT SOUNDS LIKE A CHAIR THUMPING AROUND THE ROOM.

BONK BONK

WELL, HIS DINNER IS STONE COLD. I HOPE HE'S HAPPY.

ALL RIGHT, YOUNG MAN! YOU'VE WASTED THE NICE MEAL YOUR MOM FIXED. GET OUT HERE.

YOU TIED YOURSELF UP?? WHAT ON EARTH WERE YOU DOING?!

HOBBES TIED ME UP, DAD! IT'S HIS FAULT!

DON'T MAKE UP LIES, CALVIN. HOW DID YOU GET YOURSELF LIKE THIS?!

HOBBES DID IT, DAD! HE WAS GOING TO HOLD ME FOR RANSOM! HONEST!

RANSOM?? WHO'D PAY FOR YOU, YOU BIG FIBBER?! I'M CERTAINLY GLAD YOUR DAD SAW THROUGH THAT FILTHY LIE!

OH, HUSH. YOU ALWAYS GET ME IN TROUBLE.

Calvin and Hobbes by WATERSON

First there was nothing...

...then there was Calvin!

Calvin, the mighty god, creates the universe with pure will!

From utter nothingness comes swirling form! Life begins where once was void!

But Calvin is no kind and loving god! He's one of the old gods! He demands sacrifice!

Yes, Calvin is a god of the underworld! And the puny inhabitants of earth displease him!

The great Calvin ignores their pleas for mercy and the doomed writhe in agony!

HAVE YOU SEEN HOW ABSORBED CALVIN IS WITH THOSE TINKERTOYS? HE'S CREATING WHOLE WORLDS OVER THERE!

I'LL BET HE GROWS UP TO BE AN ARCHITECT.

BEHOLD THE TERRIBLE THUNDER LIZARD, TYRANNOSAURUS REX!

THE FIERCEST DINOSAUR OF ALL, HE IS TWENTY TONS OF BONE-CRUSHING MUSCLE AND RAZOR-SHARP TEETH!

ALWAYS THE VICTOR, HE LETS OUT A TRIUMPHANT ROAR!

LIBRARY

BOOT

AH.. AH.. AH..

I JUTH *HADE* IT WHED THITH HAPPEDTH.

CALVIN THE CRIMINAL IS ABOUT TO FACE JUSTICE! ANGRY THRONGS TURN OUT TO WATCH HIS EXECUTION!

AS HE IS LED UP THE GALLOWS, HE REFLECTS UPON HIS MANY HEINOUS CRIMES. HE IS NOT REPENTANT!

THE NOOSE IS PUT AROUND HIS NECK AND TIGHTENED! THIS IS THE END!

GACKK URRGHH

OH, KNOCK IT OFF. SOME OF US HAVE TO WEAR A TIE EVERY DAY.

Calvin and Hobbes

by WATTERSON

SCRITCH SCRATCH

RUB RUB RUB

SHOOF SHOOF SHOOF

ITCH ITCH ITCH ITCH

THAT SIGH OUGHT TO GET ME OUT OF A FEW YEARS' PURGATORY.

HOW WAS THE KIDDY MATINEE MOVIE?

MOVIE? OH, YEAH, THE MOVIE. YEAH, THERE WAS A MOVIE. IT WAS OK, I GUESS.

HOW WAS THE MATINEE?

WE... ARE... BUYING... A VIDEO PLAYER.

"OPEN YOUR MOUTH AND CLOSE YOUR EYES, AND YOU WILL GET A BIG SURPRISE."

READY? HERE IT.... HEY! YOU'RE PEEKING!

WHAT'S THE MATTER? DON'T YOU TRUST YOUR OWN KID?! C'MON, CLOSE YOUR EYES!

UH-OH. HANG ON, HE GOT AWAY.

ANYTHING YET?

NOT ONE SNOWFLAKE.

96

Dear Santa,

Attached is my Christmas list for this year.

Last year I did not receive several items from my list.

For your convenience, I have grouped those items together on page 12. Please check them carefully, and include them with the rest of my loot this year.

THAT'S THE PROBLEM WITH THIS GUY. HE'S GOTTEN SLOPPY WITHOUT ANY COMPETITION.

♪ HE SEES YOU WHEN YOU'RE SLEEPING, HE KNOWS WHEN YOU'RE AWAKE ... ♪

HE KNOWS IF YOU'VE BEEN BAD OR GOOD, SO BE GOOD FOR GOODNESS SAKE! ♪

* CLICK *

SANTA CLAUS: KINDLY OLD ELF, OR CIA SPOOK?

THIS SANTA CLAUS STUFF BOTHERS ME.... ESPECIALLY THE JUDGE AND JURY BIT.

WHO APPOINTED SANTA? HOW DO WE KNOW HE'S IMPARTIAL? WHAT CRITERIA DOES HE USE FOR DETERMINING GOOD AND BAD?

AND WHAT ABOUT EXTENUATING CIRCUMSTANCES? KIDS SHOULD HAVE THE BENEFIT OF LEGAL COUNSEL, DON'T YOU THINK?

YOU'RE WORRIED ABOUT THE SALAMANDER INCIDENT, AREN'T YOU?

TEMPORARY INSANITY! THAT'S ALL IT WAS!

THEY SAY SANTA KNOWS IF YOU'VE BEEN GOOD OR BAD, BUT WHAT IF SOMEONE HAD BEEN SORT OF *BOTH?*

I MEAN, SUPPOSE SOME KID *TRIED* TO BE GOOD...AT LEAST, WELL, MOST OF THE TIME...BUT BAD THINGS INEXPLICABLY KEPT HAPPENING?

SUPPOSE SOME KID JUST HAD TERRIBLE LUCK, AND HE GOT BLAMED FOR A LOT OF THINGS HE DID ONLY *SORT* OF ON PURPOSE?

WHO EXACTLY MIGHT WE BE TALKING ABOUT?

THIS IS A PURELY HYPOTHETICAL CASE, MR. SMARTY PANTS.

THIS WHOLE SANTA CLAUS THING JUST DOESN'T MAKE SENSE.

WHY ALL THE SECRECY? WHY ALL THE MYSTERY? IF THE GUY EXISTS, WHY DOESN'T HE EVER SHOW HIMSELF AND PROVE IT?

AND IF HE *DOESN'T* EXIST, WHAT'S THE MEANING OF ALL THIS?

I DUNNO... ISN'T THIS A RELIGIOUS HOLIDAY?

YEAH, BUT ACTUALLY, I'VE GOT THE SAME QUESTIONS ABOUT GOD.

GOSH, HOBBES, WHAT IF I DON'T GET ANY PRESENTS THIS YEAR BECAUSE I DOUBTED THE EXISTENCE OF SANTA?

SUPPOSE HE'S PUTTING MY NAME ON THE "BAD" LIST RIGHT NOW! THAT WOULD BE AWFUL!

PERSONALLY, I'D THINK THAT IF YOU WEREN'T ON THE "BAD" LIST ALL ALONG, THIS WOULDN'T PUSH YOU OVER.

THANKS FOR THE COMFORT, EGGNOG BRAIN.

SEE? *SEE* WHY YOU'RE ON THE "BAD" LIST? INSULTS!

WELL, I'VE DECIDED I *DO* BELIEVE IN SANTA CLAUS, NO MATTER HOW PREPOSTEROUS HE SOUNDS.

WHAT CONVINCED YOU?

A SIMPLE RISK ANALYSIS.

I WANT PRESENTS. *LOTS* OF PRESENTS. WHY RISK NOT GETTING THEM OVER A MATTER OF BELIEF? HECK, I'LL BELIEVE ANYTHING THEY WANT.

HOW CYNICALLY ENTERPRISING OF YOU.

IT'S THE SPIRIT OF CHRISTMAS.

PSST! ARE YOU AWAKE?

OF COURSE.

I HAVEN'T HEARD SANTA YET, HAVE YOU? DO YOU THINK HE'S COMING?

IT'S ONLY 11:00. WE MAY BE LATER ON THE ROUTE.

THUMP!

GASP DID YOU HEAR THAT?

IT'S HIM! IT'S SANTA! SHHH! HE'S SAYING SOMETHING!

SLIPPIN' RIPPIN' DANG FANG ROTTEN ZARG BARG-A-DING DONG!

QUIET, DEAR! CALVIN WILL HEAR YOU!

WE GOT PRESENTS! SANTA CAME! HE CAME! HE CAME!

OH, NO... IT'S NOT MORNING ALREADY?

WELL, TECHNICALLY, YES...

Calvin and Hobbes

by WATTERSON

Calvin: HERE'S A BOX OF CRAYONS. I NEED SOME ILLUSTRATIONS FOR A STORY I'M WRITING.

Calvin: YOU CAN DRAW SOMETHING BESIDES TIGERS, CAN'T YOU?

Hobbes: SURE. LEOPARDS, PUMAS, OCELOTS.. ..YOU NAME IT.

Calvin: HERE, DAD, READ *THIS* STORY TONIGHT. I WROTE IT AND HOBBES ILLUSTRATED IT.

Dad: ..UM... OK.

Dad: "THE DAD WHO LIVED TO REGRET BEING MEAN TO HIS KID."

Calvin: WHAT ARE YOU PAUSING FOR? KEEP READING.

Barney's dad was really bad,
So Barney hatched a plan.
When his dad said, "Eat your peas!"
Barney shouted, "NO!" and ran.

peas

Barney

Barney tricked his mean ol' dad,
And locked him in the cellar.
His mom never found out
where he'd gone,
'Cause Barney didn't tell her.

door

key

There his dad spent his life,
Eating mice and gruel.
With every bite for fifty years
He was sorry he'd been cruel.
THE END.

Barney's dad

mice

Calvin: YOU KNOW HOW A LOT OF STORIES HAVE MORALS TO THEM...?

Dad: I *GET* IT, I *GET* IT!

WATTERSON & HOBS

WHAT DO YOU THINK IS THE MEANING OF TRUE HAPPINESS?

IS IT MONEY, CARS AND WOMEN?

..OR IS IT JUST MONEY AND CARS?

WELL-L-L-L?

LOOK AT THIS! YOU CALL THIS SNOW?!

IT'S NOT EVEN AN INCH HIGH! WHAT GOOD IS LESS THAN AN INCH OF SNOW?!

WELL, IT'S PRETTY.

NOBODY EVER CLOSED A SCHOOL ON ACCOUNT OF PRETTINESS.

MY SNOW FORT MAKES ME INVULNERABLE!

FROM BEHIND ITS THICK WALL, I CAN LAUNCH A BRUTAL SNOWBALL BARRAGE AND REMAIN SAFE FROM RETALIATION!

WHAP!

YOU'RE SUPPOSED TO ATTACK FROM *THAT* SIDE OF THE FORT, DUMMY!!

I HATE WAITING FOR THE SCHOOL BUS ON DAYS LIKE THESE.

BLUSTERY COLD DAYS SHOULD BE SPENT PROPPED UP IN BED WITH A MUG OF HOT CHOCOLATE AND A PILE OF COMIC BOOKS.

THAT'S WHAT I'D LIKE TO BE DOING RIGHT NOW.

AS SOON AS I GRADUATE, I'M GOING TO SPEND *EVERY* WINTER THAT WAY.

I WISH YOUR BUS WOULD COME. MY HOT CHOCOLATE WILL GET COLD.

ARE YOU JUST GOING TO SIT INSIDE ALL DAY?

YOU SHOULD GO PLAY OUTSIDE AND GET SOME FRESH AIR!

HELP ME FIGURE OUT THIS HOMEWORK PROBLEM, HOBBES. WHAT'S 3 + 8?

OK, ASSIGN THE ANSWER A VALUE OF "X". "X" ALWAYS MEANS MULTIPLY, SO TAKE THE NUMERATOR (THAT'S LATIN FOR "NUMBER EIGHTER") AND PUT THAT ON THE OTHER SIDE OF THE EQUATION.

THAT LEAVES YOU WITH THREE ON THIS SIDE, SO WHAT TIMES THREE EQUALS EIGHT? THE ANSWER, OF COURSE, IS SIX.

GOSH, I MUST HAVE DONE ALL THE OTHERS WRONG.

THESE PROBLEMS SEEM AWFULLY ADVANCED FOR FIRST GRADE, IF YOU ASK ME.

WATTERSON

HERE'S ANOTHER MATH PROBLEM I CAN'T FIGURE OUT. WHAT'S 9 + 4?

OOH, THAT'S A TRICKY ONE. YOU HAVE TO USE CALCULUS AND IMAGINARY NUMBERS FOR THIS.

IMAGINARY NUMBERS?!

YOU KNOW, ELEVENTEEN, THIRTY-TWELVE, AND ALL THOSE. IT'S A LITTLE CONFUSING AT FIRST.

HOW DID YOU LEARN ALL THIS? YOU'VE NEVER EVEN GONE TO SCHOOL!

INSTINCT. TIGERS ARE BORN WITH IT.

WATTERSON

HEAVE A ROCK AT ME

IT'S FREEZING IN THIS HOUSE! SOMEBODY CRANK UP THE THERMOSTAT! WHY DOESN'T SOMEONE MAKE A FIRE?!

IF WE CAN'T AFFORD TO HEAT THIS PLACE, MAYBE DAD SHOULD GET A BETTER JOB! WHY CAN'T WE MOVE TO FLORIDA?!

CALVIN, PIPE DOWN AND PUT ON A SWEATER IF YOU'RE COLD.

AND GO TO ALL THAT TROUBLE?!

I READ THAT THE AVERAGE HOUSEHOLD WATCHES 7½ HOURS OF TV EVERY DAY.

MOM SAYS SHE DOESN'T WATCH TV AT ALL WHILE I'M AT SCHOOL...

...SO IF I GET HOME AT 3:00, I SHOULD BE ABLE TO WATCH IT STRAIGHT TILL 10:30, RIGHT?

WRONG.

DO YOU WANT US TO BE SUB-AVERAGE?!

MOM, THE WASHER IS DONE.

OK.

AREN'T YOU GOING TO PUT THE WASH IN THE DRYER?

IN A MINUTE.

YOU MEAN YOU'RE JUST GOING TO LET IT SIT IN THE WASHING MACHINE?!?

CALVIN, CAN'T YOU SEE I'M BUSY RIGHT NOW??

SHE SAYS SHE'S BUSY.

I HOPE THE NEXT TIME SHE TAKES A BATH THERE AREN'T ANY TOWELS.

CALVIN and HOBBES by WATTERSON

TWO PARTS SLUSH...
ONE PART SOLID ICE...
ONE PART HARD-PACKED SNOW...
A DASH OF ASSORTED DEBRIS...

SCULPT INTO SPHERE, AND SERVE AT HIGH VELOCITY WITHOUT WARNING.

OH, BOY, HERE COMES SUSIE!

HEY, SUSIE!

WHAP!

HA HA! I GOTCHA, YOU DUMB GIRL!!

AUGHH! MY EYEBALL! WHERE'S MY EYEBALL?!

WHAT ARE YOU TALKING ABOUT? I HIT YOU IN THE BACK.

IT KNOCKED MY EYEBALL OUT! FIND IT AND PACK IT IN SNOW SO THEY CAN SAVE IT! OW! OW!

GOSH, DID YOU REALLY LOSE YOUR EYEBALL? I DIDN'T KNOW THEY CAME OUT! WOW. I'M REALLY SORRY. I DIDN'T MEAN TO KNOCK IT OUT. CAN I SEE THE SOCKET? BOY, WHERE DO YOU SUPPOSE IT ROLLED?

WATTERSON

SOMEWHERE OVER THERE, POOP HEAD!!

BOOT

WHAT ARE YOU DOING?

MY EYEBALL FELL OUT. HELP ME LOOK FOR IT.

WHO'S COMING TO VISIT? YOUR UNCLE MAX. I THOUGHT I TOLD YOU.

UNCLE MAX?? *I* DON'T REMEMBER ANY UNCLE MAX. ARE YOU SURE HE'S RELATED? MAYBE HE'S A CON MAN TRYING TO SWINDLE US!

OF COURSE HE'S RELATED. HE'S YOUR DAD'S BROTHER. HE JUST HASN'T BEEN HERE FOR A FEW YEARS.

WHY NOT? WAS HE IN JAIL? NO! GOOD HEAVENS, CALVIN.

NOW, NOW... WITH MAX, THAT'S NOT A BAD GUESS.

WE'RE GETTING NEAR THE AIRPORT, CALVIN. SEE THE JETS?

HOW COME YOU'RE SO QUIET BACK THERE? AREN'T YOU EXCITED TO SEE UNCLE MAX?

...YEAH...

I JUST HOPE NOBODY THINKS I'M GIVING UP *MY* ROOM WHILE HE'S HERE.

IT'S GREAT TO SEE YOU, MAX! IT SEEMS LIKE AGES SINCE YOU'VE BEEN HERE.

I'LL SAY.

I DIDN'T THINK IT HAD BEEN SO LONG, UNTIL I SAW CALVIN. THIS GUY HAS REALLY GROWN.

SO KID, WHAT DO YOU SAY?

I SAY YOU'D BETTER WATCH YOUR STEP, 'CAUSE I'VE GOT A LIVE, MAN-EATING TIGER AT HOME, AND IF I SO MUCH AS WINK, HE'LL RIP YOUR LUNGS OUT.

CUTE KID, BRO.

AND THIS IS **MY** ROOM, UNCLE MAX. I DON'T KNOW WHERE YOU'RE SLEEPING, BUT IT SURE ISN'T HERE.

GOTCHA. NICE ROOM.

THIS IS HOBBES. I WOULDN'T GET TOO CLOSE IF I WAS YOU.

DON'T WORRY. HE LOOKS LIKE A FIERCE ONE.

YEP. MANDIBLES OF DEATH, THAT'S WHAT HE'S GOT.

...AND A KILLER'S EYE. YOU CAN TELL. I...I THINK I'LL GO DOWNSTAIRS.

OL' UNCLE MAX SEEMS PRETTY SHARP. HARD TO BELIEVE HE'S RELATED TO DAD.

"A KILLER'S EYE," HE SAID. WOW! I WONDER WHICH ONE!

HEY! HEY, KID, WHAT ARE YOU DOING?!

I'M GOING THROUGH YOUR LUGGAGE. WHAT'S IT LOOK LIKE I'M DOING?

DID MOMMY AND DADDY RAISE YOU THEMSELVES, OR DID THEY JUST UNTIE YOU FOR MY VISIT?

DIDN'T YOU BRING ME A PRESENT? I CAN'T FIND ONE ANYWHERE.

IS THIS MY PLACE? CAN'T I SIT OVER THERE? I WANT TO SIT NEXT TO UNCLE MAX. CAN I? PLEASE? PLEASE?

OK, GO AHEAD. MOVE YOUR CHAIR OVER.

YOU SHOULD BE FLATTERED, MAX. CALVIN ASKED TO SIT BY YOU TONIGHT.

HEY, THAT'S SWEET.

THBBPTH·BPT!

DO YOU HAVE ANY KIDS, UNCLE MAX?

ME? NOPE, I'M NOT EVEN MARRIED.

OH.

...WHAT DIFFERENCE DOES *THAT* MAKE?

KID WATCHES A LOT OF TV, DOES HE?

BOY, CALVIN TAKES THAT STUFFED TIGER EVERYWHERE HE GOES.

YEAH, THEY'RE INSEPARABLE.

DO YOU WORRY ABOUT THAT? I MEAN, SHOULDN'T HE BE PLAYING WITH REAL FRIENDS?

OH, I THINK HE WILL WHEN HE'S READY. DIDN'T YOU EVER HAVE AN IMAGINARY FRIEND?

SOMETIMES I THINK *ALL* MY FRIENDS HAVE BEEN IMAGINARY.

UNCLE MAX, LOOK! I'LL SHOW YOU A MAGIC DISAPPEARING TRICK!

OK, FIRST I'LL NEED AN ORDINARY TWENTY-DOLLAR BILL.

HOW ABOUT IF I LEND YOU A NICKEL INSTEAD?

NO, IT WORKS MUCH BETTER WITH A TWENTY. ...OR A FIFTY, IF YOU HAVE ONE.

I TAKE IT YOU THINK YOUR OL' UNCLE MAX IS A LOW-WATT BULB.

WHY, DID DAD TELL YOU HOW THIS WORKS?

WHEN ARE YOU GOING BACK HOME, UNCLE MAX?

TOMORROW. IS THAT SOON ENOUGH?

GEE, I WISH YOU COULD STAY FOREVER.

WHAT A NICE THING TO SAY! YOU'RE ALL RIGHT, CALVIN.

MOM'S A LOT MORE PATIENT WITH ME IN FRONT OF GUESTS.

WELL, SO LONG, MAX. IT WAS GREAT TO SEE YOU AGAIN.

YOU, TOO. HAVE A SAFE TRIP HOME.

COME VISIT ME SOMETIME, OK, FELLA?

HECK, I'LL COME RIGHT NOW! SO LONG, MOM! BYE, DAD!

CALVIN, GET BACK HERE!

I NEVER GET TO DO ANYTHING FUN.

MISSED YOUR CHANCE DEAR. WE COULD'VE BOUGHT HIM A TICKET.

WELL...

Z

112

Calvin and Hobbes by WATTERSON

I'VE GOT TO GO IN. ANOTHER FIVE MINUTES OUT HERE, AND I'LL BE FROZEN SOLID.

GOSH, I HOPE THAT WAS NO ONE I KNEW.

YOU LOOKED PRETTY COLD COMING UP THE HILL, SO I FIXED YOU SOME HOT CHOCOLATE AND CRACKERS WITH PEANUT BUTTER.

GO WRAP UP IN A BLANKET AND TAKE THESE IN FRONT OF THE FIRE.

HERE'S HOBBES AND A COMIC BOOK. GETTING TOASTY?

UH HUH. THANKS.

SHE EVEN PUT MARSHMALLOWS IN THE HOT CHOCOLATE.

NOBODY KNOWS HOW TO PAMPER LIKE A MOM.

SO ARE YOU GOING TO EAT ALL THOSE PEANUT BUTTER CRACKERS YOURSELF, OR WHAT?

WATTERSON

AAGHH, I CAN'T BELIEVE WE WERE ASSIGNED TO DO A REPORT TOGETHER.

ALL I CAN SAY IS YOU'D BETTER DO A GREAT JOB! I DON'T WANT TO FLUNK JUST BECAUSE I WAS ASSIGNED A DOOFUS FOR A PARTNER.

A DOOFUS ?? WHO TAKES HER SANDWICHES APART AND EATS EACH INGREDIENT SEPARATELY?

WHAT'S WRONG WITH THAT?!

IT CERTIFIES YOU AS A GRADE "A" NIMROD.

IT DOES NOT!

OK, LOOK. WE'VE GOT TO DO THIS DUMB PROJECT TOGETHER, SO WE MIGHT AS WELL GET IT OVER WITH. WHAT ARE WE SUPPOSED TO BE DOING?

WEREN'T YOU EVEN PAYING ATTENTION?! WHAT WOULD YOU DO IF I WASN'T HERE TO ASK?? YOU'D FLUNK AND BE SENT BACK TO KINDERGARTEN, THAT'S WHAT!

SAYS YOU! I HEARD THAT SOMETIMES KIDS DON'T PAY ATTENTION BECAUSE THE CLASS GOES AT TOO SLOW OF A PACE FOR THEM. SOME OF US ARE TOO SMART FOR THE CLASS.

OH, RIGHT. YOU'RE TOO SMART.

BELIEVE IT, LADY. YOU KNOW HOW EINSTEIN GOT BAD GRADES AS A KID? WELL, MINE ARE EVEN WORSE!

SO WHAT ARE WE SUPPOSED TO BE DOING?

WE'RE SUPPOSED TO BE RESEARCHING THE PLANET MERCURY.

SO WHAT HAVE WE FOUND OUT?

NOTHING! I'M NOT GOING TO DO THIS WHOLE THING MYSELF!

YOU'D PROBABLY GOOF IT ALL UP IF YOU DID. LET'S GET STARTED.

YES! LET'S!

I'LL BE THE MANAGEMENT, AND YOU CAN BE THE LABOR. FIRST, GET SOME BOOKS.

DOES ANYONE WANT TO TRADE PARTNERS?

WHAT ARE YOU DOING?! YOU'RE DOODLING! YOU'RE SITTING HERE DRAWING MARTIANS WHEN WE'RE SUPPOSED TO BE RESEARCHING!

YOU HAVEN'T DONE *ANYTHING* YET! DON'T YOU CARE?? WHAT'S THE MATTER WITH YOU?!

IT'S NO USE! WE'RE GOING TO FLUNK! I'LL HAVE TO GO TO A SECOND-RATE COLLEGE BECAUSE MY IDIOT PARTNER SPENT THE STUDY PERIOD DRAWING MARTIANS!

WHY ME? WHY ME? WHY ME?

HERE, THIS WILL CHEER YOU UP. THE MARTIAN MOVES WHEN YOU FLIP THE PAGES! WATCH, YOU CAN SEE HIM EAT AN ASTRONAUT!

LOOK, BIRD BRAIN, YOU WASTED THIS ENTIRE WEEK IN THE LIBRARY.

WE HAVE TO GIVE OUR REPORT ON MONDAY. YOU'D BETTER BUST YOUR BUTT OVER THE WEEKEND, OR I'M TELLING THE TEACHER YOU DIDN'T DO ANY WORK. GOT IT?

...WELL, WHAT DO YOU SAY?! AM I GETTING THROUGH TO YOU?? THIS IS IMPORTANT!

GRONK! GRIBBLE GOK! GAK GORK! GOONK!!

OUR HERO REGARDS THE STRANGE ALIEN. ...IT SEEMS TO BE TRYING TO COMMUNICATE.

CALVIN, TELEPHONE!

WHY AREN'T YOU AT THE LIBRARY?!?

WE HAVE TO GIVE OUR REPORT ON PLANET MERCURY TODAY. DID YOU DO YOUR HALF?

OF COURSE I DID. AND I'LL BET MY HALF MAKES YOUR HALF LOOK PATHETIC.

IT HAD **BETTER** BE GOOD... OR ELSE!

THE PLANET MERCURY
An Exhaustively Researched Report by Calvin

"...AND SO, THE PLANET MERCURY IS A HOT AND BARREN WORLD, THE CLOSEST TO OUR SUN."

AND TO TELL US ABOUT THE MYTHOLOGY OF MERCURY, HERE'S MY PARTNER, CALVIN.

THANK YOU, THANK YOU! HEY, WHAT A CROWD! YOU LOOK GREAT THIS MORNING... REALLY, I MEAN THAT! GO ON, GIVE YOURSELVES A HAND!

YOU KNOW, A FUNNY THING HAPPENED ON THE WAY TO THE LIBRARY YESTERDAY...

THIS ISN'T MY FAULT, MISS WORMWOOD!

THE PLANET MERCURY WAS NAMED AFTER A ROMAN GOD WITH WINGED FEET.

MERCURY WAS THE GOD OF FLOWERS AND BOUQUETS, WHICH IS WHY TODAY HE IS A REGISTERED TRADEMARK OF FTD FLORISTS.

WHY THEY NAMED A PLANET AFTER THIS GUY, I CAN'T IMAGINE.

...UM... BACK TO YOU, SUSIE.

BOY, YOU SHOULD'VE SEEN THE SPARKS FLY WHEN I GAVE MY HALF OF THE REPORT.

I'VE NEVER SEEN SUSIE SO MAD. SHE ACCUSED ME OF NOT DOING ANY RESEARCH AND CLAIMED I MADE UP THE WHOLE THING.

DID YOU?

HECK, NO. I JUST TOOK A FEW CREATIVE LIBERTIES.

AND THEY CALLED YOUR MOM OVER A FEW CREATIVE LIBERTIES?

GEEZ, YOU THINK *SUSIE* WAS MAD...

DON'T YOU HATE IT WHEN YOUR BOOGERS FREEZE?

HERE WE ARE, OVERLOOKING SUICIDE GULCH, ABOUT TO HURL OURSELVES DOWN AT BREAKNECK SPEED IN A SLED THAT HARDLY STEERS!

RISKING LIFE AND LIMB! LOOKING DEATH STRAIGHT IN THE EYE!

"WHY?" YOU ASK! WHY DO WE DO IT??

BECAUSE WE GET PAID, I HOPE.

BECAUSE IT'S THERE!

LOOK, HOBBES, THE LATEST PERFECTION IN TECHNOLOGY.

A WATER PISTOL?

HECK, NO! THIS IS THE NEW, IMPROVED VERSION OF THE TRANSMOGRIFIER.

NOW YOU CAN TRANSMOGRIFY THINGS JUST BY POINTING AT THEM! SAY YOU DON'T LIKE THE COLOR OF YOUR BEDSPREAD. WELL, YOU JUST ZAP IT, AND PRESTO, IT'S AN IGUANA!

ONE CAN CERTAINLY IMAGINE THE MYRIAD OF USES FOR A HAND-HELD IGUANA MAKER.

IT DOESN'T *HAVE* TO BE AN IGUANA. IT CAN BE ANYTHING. SUPPOSE MOM'S GETTING ON OUR NERVES, FOR INSTANCE...

HOW DOES THIS TRANSMOGRIFIER GUN KNOW WHAT TO TRANSMOGRIFY SOMETHING INTO?

TELEPATHY.

THE GUN AUTOMATICALLY READS THE BRAIN WAVES YOU EMIT, AND TURNS THE OBJECT INTO WHATEVER YOU WANT.

THAT'S AMAZING.

WELL, IT TOOK ME ALL MORNING TO INVENT.

SO SAY I'M THINKING ABOUT A BIG SLAB OF GRILLED TUNA NOW...

WATCH WHERE YOU'RE POINTING THAT! WATCH WHERE YOU'RE POINTING THAT!

OK, LET'S TEST THIS TRANSMOGRIFIER GUN.

I WANT TO BE A PTERODACTYL, SO YOU THINK OF ONE AND POINT THE TRANSMOGRIFIER AT ME.

THIS WILL BE GREAT. I'LL TERRORIZE THE NEIGHBORHOOD AWHILE AND THEN YOU CAN TRANSMOGRIFY ME BACK TO A BOY WHEN THE NATIONAL GUARD COMES.

WHAT'S A PTERODACTYL? SOME KIND OF BUG?

NO NO! IT'S A BIG FLYING DINOSAUR! DON'T SHOOT IF YOU DON'T KNOW WHAT IT IS!!

Calvin and Hobbes

by WATTERSON

THERE! NOW WE'RE *BOTH* TRANSMOGRIFIED. WE'RE EVEN!

EVEN?? WE WOULD BE EVEN ONLY IF TURNING A TIGER INTO A DUCK WAS AN IMPROVEMENT.

THIS WASN'T AT ALL WHAT I HAD IN MIND WHEN I ASKED YOU TO TRANSMOGRIFY ME INTO A PTERODACTYL. PTERODACTYLS ARE *BIG!*

SO YOU TURNED ME INTO A DUCK, IS THAT IT?

FAIR'S FAIR.

OK, I'LL TAKE THE TRANSMOGRIFIER AND FIX YOU UP RIGHT.

ZAP

WHY YOU..!! GIMME THAT GUN!

THBBT!

ZAP

AN INSULT! THIS IS WORSE THAN BEFORE!!

ZAP

ZAP

ZAP

Much Later

GREAT. JUST GREAT. WHICH OF US IS CALVIN AND WHICH IS HOBBES *NOW?*

WELL I HOPE CALVIN IS *YOU*, BECAUSE HIS MOM'S GOING TO HAVE A FIT WHEN SHE SEES THIS.

LOOK, I'LL TRANSMOGRIFY YOU BACK TO A TIGER IF YOU'LL TRANSMOGRIFY ME BACK TO A KID, OK?

OK.

ZAP

AHH, THAT'S MUCH BETTER.

NOW DO ME.

CLICK...CLICK...CLICK

WHAT'S WRONG?? I'M NOT TRANSMOGRIFYING!

BOY, I'M GLAD WE DID ME FIRST.

WHAT'S WRONG WITH THE TRANSMOGRIFIER? WHY WON'T IT WORK??

YOU INVENTED IT. YOU TELL ME.

DON'T TELL ME I'M STUCK AS AN OWL FOR THE REST OF MY LIFE!

I THINK OWLS MOSTLY EAT MICE. I SUPPOSE WE COULD CATCH SOME IN THE YARD.

THIS IS AWFUL! WHAT AM I GOING TO DO?!

UGGH, I COULD NEVER EAT A MOUSE RAW. THEIR LITTLE FEET ARE PROBABLY REAL COLD GOING DOWN.

WILL YOU FORGET THE STUPID MICE AND HELP ME THINK?!?

I WONDER IF PET STORES WILL SELL YOU A MOUSE IF THEY KNOW YOU'RE GOING TO EAT IT?

HI, MOM, I'M AN OWL.

YOU DON'T LOOK LIKE A VERY *HAPPY* OWL.

NOPE. I'M NOT.

MAYBE SOME LUNCH WOULD HELP.

I DOUBT IT. I DON'T LIKE MICE.

THIS IS SOUP.

IS IT MOUSE SOUP? I DON'T LIKE MICE.

I HEARD YOU. IT'S TOMATO.

WHAT AM I GOING TO DO, HOBBES? I CAN'T BE AN OWL FOREVER!

HOW AM I GOING TO TRANSMOGRIFY BACK INTO A KID WHEN THE TRANSMOGRIFIER IS BROKEN?

MAYBE YOU SHOULD JUST LEARN TO ACCEPT THIS PREDICAMENT. IT'S NOT SO BAD BEING AN OWL INSTEAD OF A KID. ACTUALLY, IT'S PROBABLY BETTER.

BETTER?! HOW?

WELL, I NEVER QUITE KNEW HOW TO SAY THIS BEFORE, BUT LITTLE BOYS DON'T SMELL SO GOOD.

I'VE GOT TO GO TO SCHOOL TOMORROW MORNING! WHAT WILL THE KIDS SAY IF I'M AN OWL?!

OH, NO, I'M DOOMED! I'M DOOMED!

SINCE WHEN DO OWLS GO TO SCHOOL?

ZIP-A-DEE-DOO-*DAH* ZIP-A-DEE-AY! MY OH MY, WHAT A WONDERFUL DAY!

TIME TO GET UP, CALVIN. YOU DON'T WANT TO MISS THE SCHOOL BUS.

I'M NOT GOING TO SCHOOL, MOM. I'M AN OWL.

NO, YOU'RE NOT. NOW GET UP AND GET DRESSED.

I'M NOT AN OWL?

I'M NOT! I'M ME AGAIN! THE TRANSMOGRIFICATION MUST ONLY BE TEMPORARY! IT WORE OFF OVERNIGHT! I'M A KID! I CAN...

...GO...TO... SCHOOL.

..YAWWWNN.. KEEP THE SHADE DOWN WHEN YOU GO, OK?

The End